THE FLORA STEVENSON SCHOOL

The Last Thesaurus

Paul Muldoon was educated at Queen's University, Belfast, and then worked as a radio producer for the BBC in Northern Ireland. He now lives in America with his wife and young daughter and teaches at Princeton University.

by the same author

NEW WEATHER
MULES
WHY BROWNLEE LEFT
QUOOF
SELECTED POEMS 1968–83
MEETING THE BRITISH
MADOC
SHINING BROW
THE ANNALS OF CHILE

THE FABER BOOK OF
CONTEMPORARY IRISH POETRY (*editor*)

Paul Muldoon

The Last Thesaurus

illustrated by Rodney Rigby

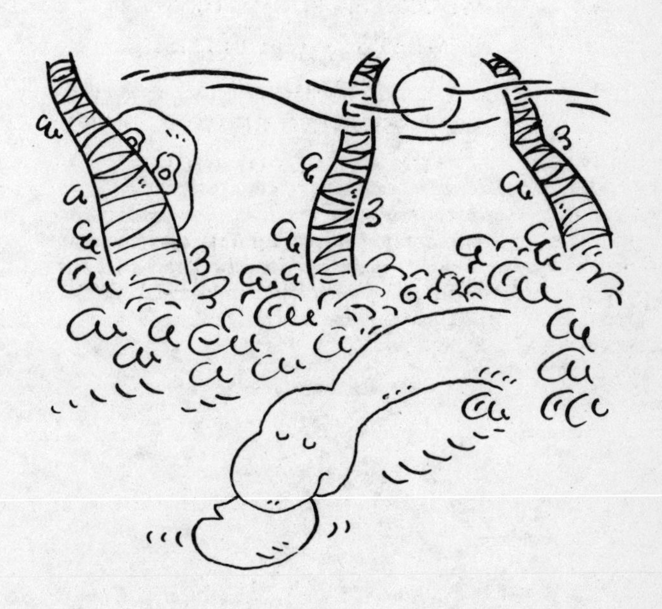

faber and faber
LONDON · BOSTON

First published in 1995
by Faber and Faber Limited
3 Queen Square London WC1N 3AU
This paperback edition first published in 1996

Phototypeset by Wilmaset Ltd, Wirral
Printed and bound in Great Britain by
Mackays of Chatham PLC, Chatham, Kent

All rights reserved

© Paul Muldoon, 1995
Illustrations © Rodney Rigby, 1995

Paul Muldoon is hereby identified as author of this work in accordance with Section 77 of the Copyright, Designs and Patents Act 1988

This book is sold subject to the condition that it shall not, by way of trade or otherwise, be lent, resold, hired out or otherwise circulated without the publisher's prior consent in any form of binding or cover other than that in which it is published and without a similar condition including this condition being imposed on the subsequent purchaser

A CIP record for this book
is available from the British Library

ISBN 0-571-17580-5

2 4 6 8 10 9 7 5 3 1

for Dorothy

Imagine, if you will, a planet wreathed in mist;
The sky the colour of green chartreuse,
The earth amethyst:
Giant horse-tail ferns and other, palm-like trees.

The ground itself has the consistency of chocolate
Mousse or devil's-food cake
That is even now jogged and jiggled
By a series of minor earthquakes.

As, lagging behind their own grunts and groans,
There trundle two bull-dozers
Topped by six-storey-high cranes;
This can only be Bert and Brunhilde Brontosaurus.

Brunhilde launches her Viking longship's prow
Far out beyond the sedge
And settles down to browse
On succulent water-weeds; Bert lingers by the edge.

Little do they know that, looming here, like the answer
To a question no one dares ask,
Is this most fearsome dinosaur –
Tyrannosaurus Rex.

This Torquemada, this Tamburlaine; he reigns by dint
Of his ultra-sensitive muzzle,
As finely-tuned
To the scent of blood as any heat-seeking missile.

Among the velvet-fisted, iron-gloved thistles
Bert hears an unfamiliar noise;
A double snore, then a high-pitched double whistle:
Whatever it is must have a double nose.

Bert parts the thistles with his prehensile lip
And, lo and behold,
There lies a young Thesaurus, fast asleep,
His spine embossed with gold.

Neither large nor small, nor dark nor fair,
Nor especially smooth nor hairy,
Our Thesaurus is rather less round than square;
He looks as if he's swallowed a dictionary.

Bert remarks on how one head ends in a pencil-point
And the other an eraser.
Even more striking are the eyes which, opened,
Show one pair jade, one pair of the deepest azure.

Brunhilde, meanwhile, is nibbling at the leaves
Of a Lilo-sized lily-pad;
She's still perfectly oblivious
To the danger lurking behind that khaki butte.

A double yawn. As the Thesaurus begins to speak,
Wonders of wonders, his soft snout
Religiously follows his beak;
One scribbles a word on the air, one rubs it out:

‘Hello, good morning, howdy, whoever you are,
Whatever your rank or station;
May I be so bold as to infer
That, in common with most of the Brontosaurus nation,

You lack a certain nicety, are less than scrupulous
In your use of "will" and "shall", "might" and "may",
And tend to confuse "rupees" and "roubles":
Even so, allow me to introduce yours truly, *moi*.

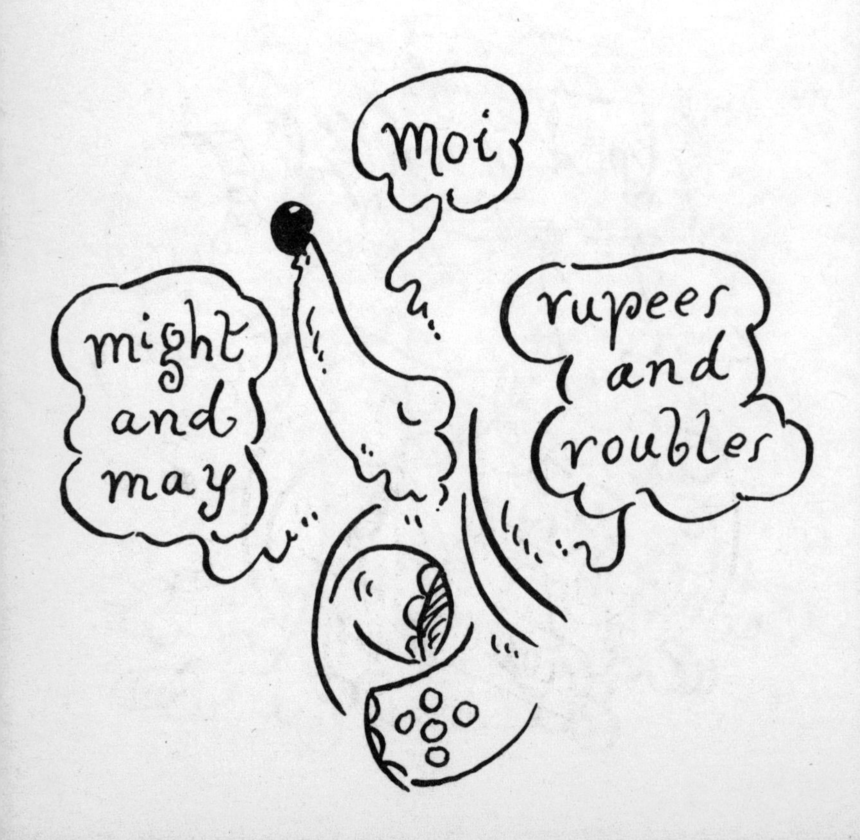

I am Theo, the last Thesaurus, the rear, the hindermost;
Before I shut up shop or hang up my fiddle
It's incumbent on me, it behooves me, I simply must
Advise and apprise you of just how futile . . .'

(Such nuances are lost on Bert, who can barely rise
To a Bronto mating-call,
While lost on both are Brunhilde's desperate cries
As the Tyranno moves in for the kill.)

'How inefficacious, to what little avail
It is to be a dinosaur,
Given the present climate. The writing's on the wall
For us, as surely as for Nebuchadnezzar.'

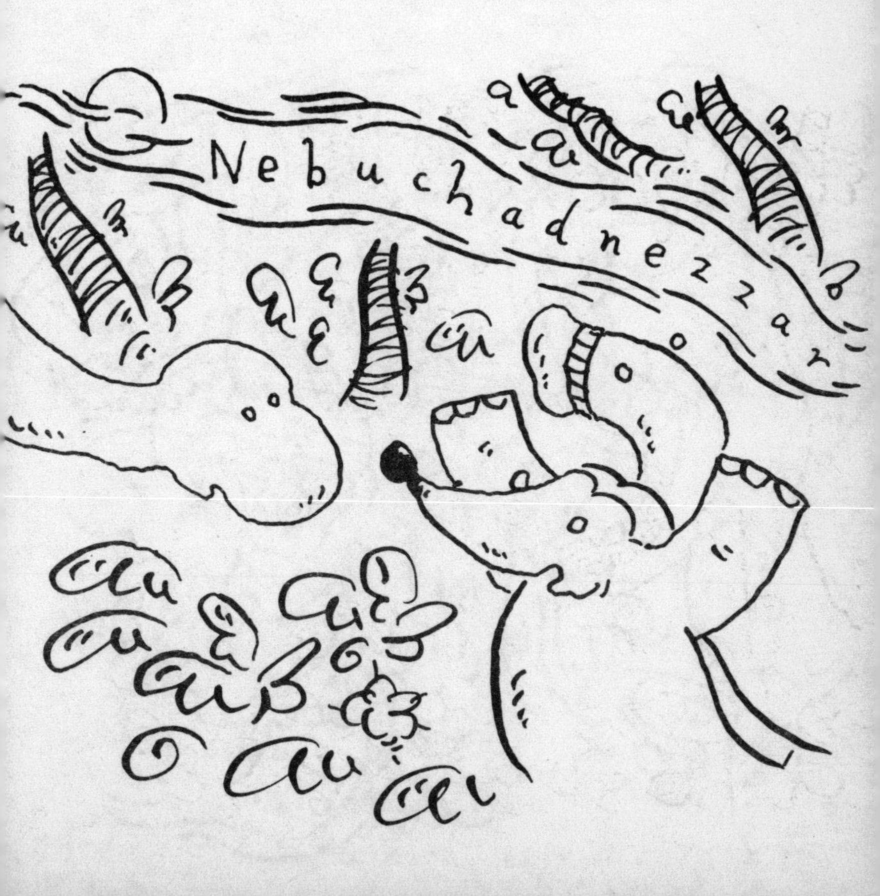

Even now, Brunhilde's shrieks
Come through loud and clear as a klaxon.
This is Theo's first glimpse of Tyrannosaurus Rex;
He mutters something faintly Anglo-Saxon.

The last Thesaurus puts his heads together
And hurriedly confers
With himself, then darts off through the heather
And stunted conifers.

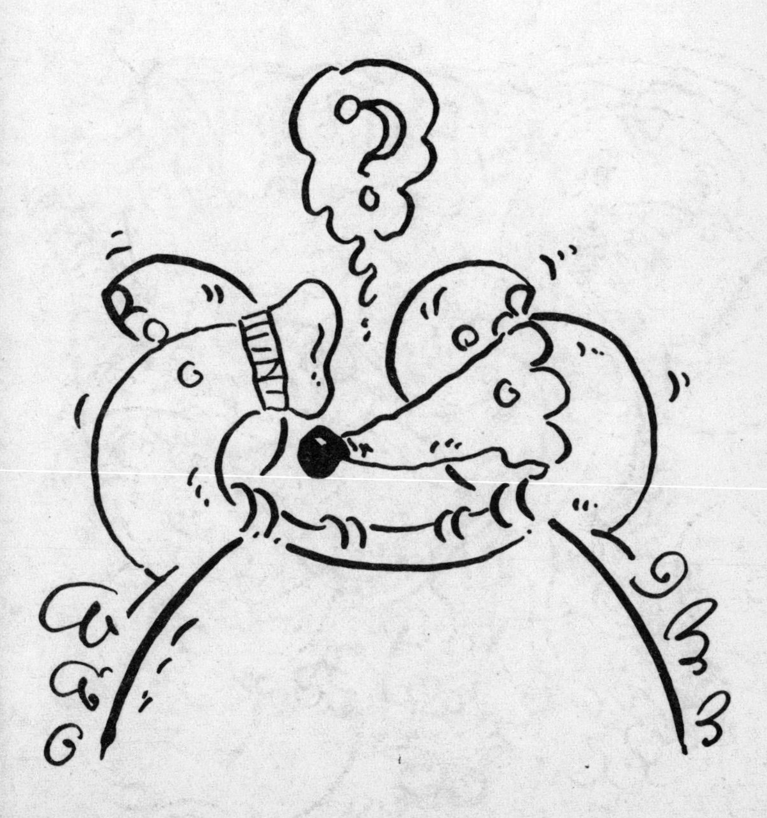

Such is his haste
That as he proceeds by leaps and bounds
A sheet of paper falls from his double breast
And flutters to the ground.

No less quick-witted than he's nimble-footed,
He somehow diverts the Tyranno's attention
By calling him 'Big Bum', 'Numbskull' and 'Fat Head',
As well as names too indelicate to mention.

Which gives Brunhilde a chance
To slope off back across the lagoon
To the osier-beds where she rejoins
Bert, who comforts her; they helplessly look on

As the Tyranno licks his chops
And flashes a toothy smile;
His jaws are reminiscent of a butcher's shop
Or the business end of a saw-mill.

The last Thesaurus is utterly alone.
Any hope of escape is vain.
Not to be outdone, he breaks off a piece of liana
Or some such sturdy vine

And somehow pole-vaults
Or catapults
Himself into the Tyranno's mouth. He then somersaults
From the epiglottis

Down the glittering esophagus
Where he lodges himself (*i.e.* sticks in the throat).
The Tyranno is now in a bind, a pickle, a fix.
However much he coughs, he cannot rid

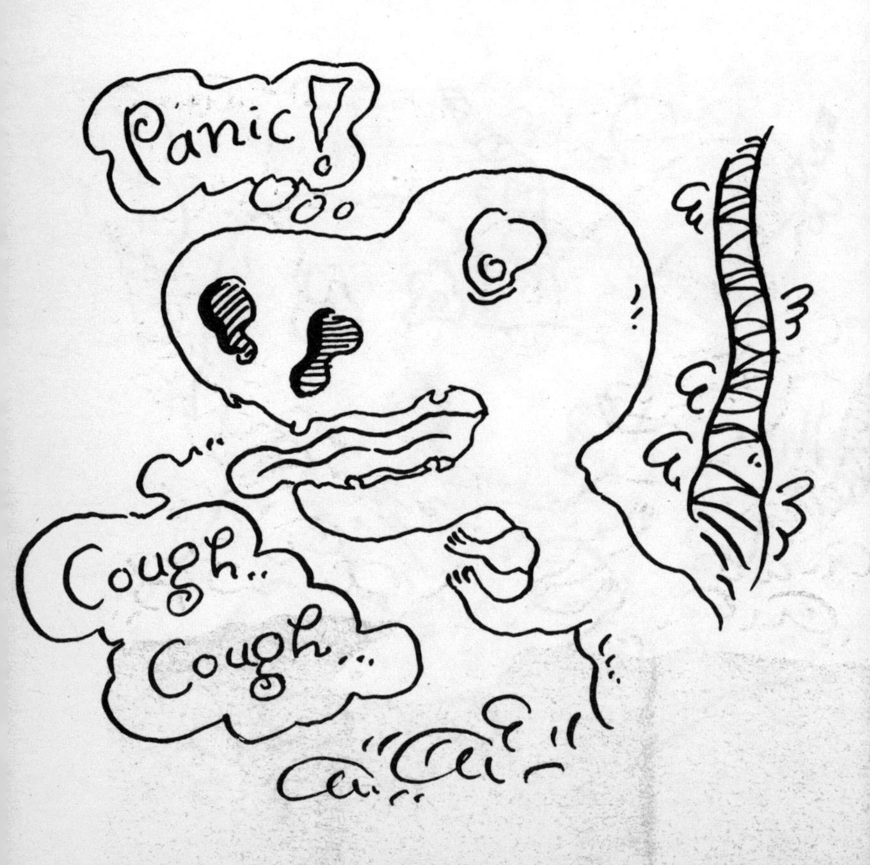

Himself of this glob, this glut, this glitch.
He kneels to drink
From a river that is, alas, a river of pitch
Into which he slowly begins to sink.

The more he strains on his anchor
The more it goes slack
Till he founders like a super-tanker
In its own oil-slick

Or a satellite
Lost in orbit
To some fabulous black hole. By the time Bert has waddled
As far as the tar-pit

Its surface is a limousine's smoked glass
That gives back zero, zilch. As the Brontosaurus
Searches for clues
He's troubled by vague misgivings, strange desires.

He wrinkles his nose. It smells like rain.
Bert is no less amazed
Than Brunhilde to hear himself mumble this refrain;
'It's incumbent on me, it behooves me, I simply must . . .'

And he imagines, as it were, a planet wreathed in mist
Which is almost a carbon-copy
Of this; all except for a wizard, Trismegist,
Who takes the form of an aardvark, a bandicoot, a coypu,

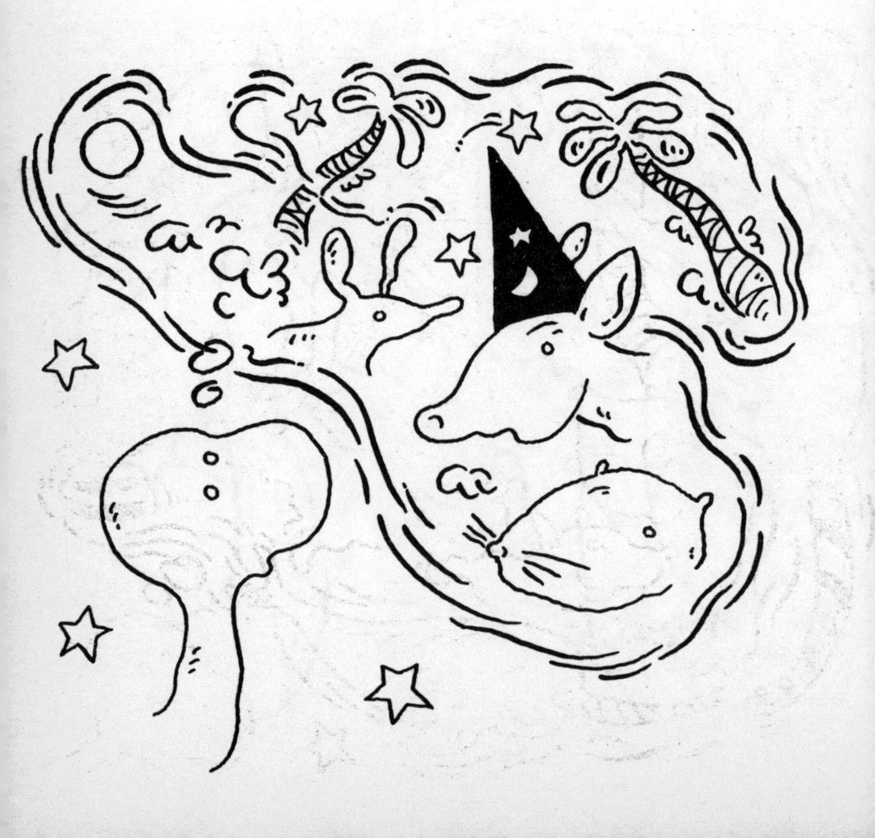

A dingo, an eland, a fox, a gnat, or a hare;
An ibex, a jennet, a kangaroo,
A lemur, a mongoose, a narwhal, an oryx, a polar bear,
A quagga, a rhino, a skunk, a tapir, or you . . .

For no sooner have *you* whispered 'Abracadabra'
Than the vicuña, the walrus, the xylophagan,
The yak and the zebra
Have vanished, faded, dissolved, gone,

And Bert's thrown back on his old, plodding self.
The rain comes down. A wind-winnowing wind
Turns over that sodden, bitter leaf
Dropped by the last Thesaurus. It reads bluntly,

The
End

A Colossal Glossary

The *aardvark*'s a kind of ant-eater, an 'earth-pig' in Dutch,
while *abracadabra* is a charm much

favoured by alchemists.
As for that wine-coloured gem, the *amethyst*,

a Greek would place it in his cup 'so as not to be drunk',
a thought no foul-mouthed *Anglo-Saxon* ever thunk.

Azure is the blue of lapis lazuli.
The *bandicoot* is a rat from Australasia

that likes to *browse* or graze on the tender shoots of rice.
A *carbon-copy*'s a replica, though only once or twice.

Yellow or green, *chartreuse* is a liqueur
distilled, as always, by monks. The *coypu*'s prized for its fur;

not so the wild dog or *dingo*.
An *eland*'s an African antelope. In medical lingo

an *epiglottis* is a tongue, an *esophagus* a gizzard.
A *glitch* would be a snag or hazard.

The *ibex* is a mountain goat; *i.e.* is short for *id est*,
in Latin 'that is'. A pain in the side

was once a *jade*, a word which
we now use of the greenish stone deemed to mend the stitch.

A *jennet* might also be a jade, in the horse-sense.
Soldiers in *khaki* uniforms tense

when they hear the siren-song of a *klaxon*,
since it almost always represents a call to action.

A *lagoon* is a shallow lake, usually on the coast.
The nocturnal *lemur* is essentially a ghost.

A *Lilo* is a rubber raft, while a *limousine*
is a vehicle whose occupants thankfully can't be seen

since they're often types who say *moi* for 'me'
and have a penchant for drinking sparkling *mongoose*-pee.

Whipped cream is the main ingredient of *mousse*.
The *narwhal* relies on its tusk when hunting Eskimos.

Nebuchadnezzar was the king of Babylon
for whom the writing on the wall was plain

as plain can be; a *nicety* may be either a subtle
or idle distinction: as such, it's its own rebuttal.

The *oryx*, like all gazelles, is thought by lions to wallow
in self-pity. An *osier* is a type of willow.

A *pickle* is anything preserved in vinegar or brine.
As one pine opined to another pitch-pine,

'He that toucheth pitch shall be defiled';
though *pitch* more commonly refers to asphalt.

The root of *prehensile* is 'prehendere', to seize;
you may already have grasped that a *quagga* is a wild ass.

The *rouble* and *rupee* are Russian and Indian coins.
To be *scrupulous* is to have qualms of conscience,

from 'scrupulus', a stone with a cutting edge;
the reed with a razor-sharp blade is *sedge*.

Tamburlaine, also known as Tamerlane or Timur,
was a Mongol king whose deportment was anything but demure,

his stock-in-trade being rapine and reprisal.
The *tapir* lives as a hermit in the rain-forests of Brazil

where it meditates on *Theo*logy;
'In the beginning was the Word, and the Word was Algae'.

A no less avid theologian was Thomas de *Torquemada*
whose cruel streak ran the gamut

from burning at the stake through hanging by a gaff
to the flaying of some fatted divinity calf –

all in the name of Truth and Justice.
On the subject of the 'thrice-great' Hermes *Trismegistus*,

or his Lord Lieutenant, Zoroaster,
my lips are sealed. I will say this; a *trundle* is a caster.

Often mistaken for a llama or alpaca, the newly-shorn *vicuña*
spits at the thought of the Norseman or *Viking*

who stole the shirt off his back. The chief
sense of *winnow* is to fan, to separate the wheat from the chaff,

the sheep from the goats, good from evil.
It's hard to categorize the *xylophagan*, this wood-boring weevil

makes of something nothing, *zilch*;
just as a worm may contain an armada, little much,

so the meanings of all the rest
of the words in this book are buried in one, a treasurechest.